SOMERSET FARMING

A HUNDRED YEARS OF CHANGE

SOMERSET FARMING

A HUNDRED YEARS OF CHANGE

An Illustrated History

By David Walker

Somerset Rural Life Museum,
Somerset County Museums Service.

Somerset Books

First published in Great Britain in 2001.

Reprinted 2001.

British Library Cataloguing-in-Publication Data
A CIP record for this title is available from the British Library

ISBN 0 86183 421 6

SOMERSET BOOKS
Official publishers to Somerset County Council

Halsgrove House
Lower Moor Way
Tiverton, Devon EX16 6SS
Tel: 01884 243242
Fax: 01884 243325
www.halsgrove.com

Printed and bound by The Cromwell Press, Trowbridge.

CONTENTS

Fordson tractor & reaper-binder, near Chard, 1940s. (P3806)

Introduction

FARMING IN SOMERSET DURING THE TWENTIETH CENTURY

What comes to mind when you think of farming? Is it past times, when one man could plough an acre a day, and everybody laboured together to bring in the harvest? Enormous changes have occurred in agriculture during the twentieth century. New technologies have altered every practice, and farming has had to respond to broader issues in society.

Traditionally agriculture is about improvement and progress. Farmers have sought to increase output and reduce the hard manual labour involved by adopting new technologies and work practices.

However, in recent years priorities are changing. Fewer and fewer people work directly in farming, and the countryside is increasingly valued for its leisure and tourism potential, its wildlife, and as an educational resource. As production subsidies decline, farmers are forced to diversify their work to survive.

Even so, today farming still plays a major part in Somerset's economy, with some 5% of the workforce dependent on agriculture.

Much of the material for this book is loaned from people involved in farming, now and in the recent past, to chart these changes across Somerset. It does not set out to be comprehensive, but is intended to be a contribution to the debate on farming today.

David Walker
Keeper – Social History
Somerset County Museums Service

Dry stone walls near Priddy, Mendip Hills, 1997. (P5052)

Newly laid hedge near Doulting, 1997. (P5055)

LANDSCAPE

The diversity of Somerset landscape is extraordinary. The limestone uplands of Mendip, the low lying Levels and Moors, Exmoor and the Quantock Hills, and the land to the south of the county, all have their own particular distinctive identity.

The special character of these places has evolved over thousands of years through the influences and patterns of landform and drainage, human habitation, farming, and industry. In such a predominantly rural county, agriculture plays a leading role in shaping the landscape.

Elm trees at Abbey Farm, Glastonbury, 1960s. (25/358)

Pollarded willows by a rhyne near
Godney, Somerset Levels, 1997.
(P5046)

Young heifers kept in by a rhyne near Glastonbury, 1994. (S6263)

GRASS

Grass grows particularly well in Somerset and the County's agriculture has always been organised to make the most of this. The general trend during the great agricultural depression which had begun during the 1870s was for the acreage of permanent grassland to increase. Grassland required less labour than arable farming, and livestock made more money than cereals.

Before the Second World War a typical Somerset dairy farm grew all grass and made hay for winter feeding, supplemented with cattle cake based on imported grain and oil by-products. This changed during the war when many acres of grassland were turned over to grain for human consumption, with roots and hay for winter fodder. The post-war development of silage has retained the importance of grass.

Mowing

1900s
Grass was commonly cut by a gang of men using scythes. By the time of the First World War horse-drawn mowers were becoming more common.

1940s
Tractor and horse-drawn reciprocating knife mowers, driven by the land wheels, were still being made.

1950s
Tractor trailed mowers were still made in the 1950s, and later superseded by tractor mounted cutter bar mowers. They were easy to use and move around the farm. The Ferguson mower made for the TE20 tractor was one of the first.

1960s
Although developed earlier, the rotary mower made little impact until the 1960s, but by the 1980s they were the norm.

Mowing with scythes, Exford, c.1900. (P638)

Mowing by hand, 1923. (P4414)

Mowing grass for hay c.1940. (350/1987/8)

Walter Hutchins on Ferguson tractor and Mrs Hutchins on mower, Hoccombe Farm,
Lydeard St Lawrence, c.1965. (Courtesy of Mrs Martin; P3464)

Bamfords leaflet, 1951. (87/1999/31)

Haymaking

1900s

Men, women and children would turn the swaths of cut grass with pitch forks until dry, and horse-drawn hay sweeps would gather the hay beside a waggon or haystack. The hay was usually pitch-forked into waggons and hay grabs were used to carry it up onto the haystacks.

1910s

Horse drawn swath-turners and tedders became more common to turn the drying cut grass, and side delivery rakes helped gather it into rows. Waggons still collected the hay, but elevators were introduced to take it up onto the haystacks.

1950s

Many horse-drawn tedders, swath-turners and side delivery rakes made in the 1930s and 1940s were converted for use with a tractor, and tractor-drawn land wheel driven rakes were still being made. The loose hay swaths were then pushed to the rick on the long wooden tines of a haysweep.

Hayrakes were used for the final clearance of the field, and mounted hayrakes gradually replaced horse and tractor drawn hayrakes during the 1950s. The pick-up bailer was also developed.

1960s

The development of finger wheel rakes, and hay conditioning crushers and crimpers speeded up the hay-making process, followed by power-driven rotary tedders, so that high speed haymaking was standard practice by the late 1970s.

Building a haystack, Exford, c.1900. (P637)

Building a haystack using a hay grab, c.1910. (P2722)

Using a hay elevator, Babington Park, near Radstock, 1913. (P426)

J. & W. Knight using a horse drawn hay rake, Middle Burnham Farm, Edithmead, Burnham-on-Sea, 1940s. (Courtesy of Mrs Drinkwater; 196/1987/10)

Bamfords leaflet, 1951. (87/1999/23)

Bamfords leaflet, 1951. (87/1999/24)

Bamfords leaflet, 1951. (87/1999/25)

Frampton family haymaking at Short Breach Farm, Ashcott, 1950s. (Courtesy of Mrs E. Frampton; P5056, P5057)

Dutch barn for hay, New Road Farm, East Huntspill, 1988. (S5808)

Makers sign on the gable of a Dutch barn at Butleigh, 1994. (SCMS)

Silaging

1940s and 1950s

Silage making was arduous and labour intensive. Cut grass was loaded into trailers with a green crop loader, or a tractor and buckrake were used to ferry the grass to a silage clamp or pit. Controlled with an electric fence, stock were allowed to help themselves from the clamp.

Grass was also baled into small bales which could be fed from mangers.

1950s

The system of making silage in towers was introduced. These glass-lined chambers were sealed with butyl rubber caps. The Frome firm of Wallington and Western Ltd became leading manufacturers of these rubber seals.

Unmanned loaders superseded rake-bar green crop loaders of the 1940s.

1960s

Flail-type forage harvesters became popular in the 1960s, but the grass cut this way was unsuitable for making silage in towers.

1970s

Trailed precision chop forage harvesters were introduced which cut the grass into shorter lengths. Self-propelled precision chop forage harvesters are expensive to run, and are mainly used by contractors. As an alternative to the silage clamp, big round bales of the cut grass are wrapped in black polythene sheeting in which the silage forms.

Cows feeding in a silage clamp, New Road Farm, East Huntspill, 1988. (S5804)

Forage harvesting grass for silage, Hurlingpot Farm, 1987. (SCMS)

The dairy herd requires a continuous supply of highly nutritive fodder throughout the year, and in Somerset milk yields have risen since the Second World War in response to refinements in feeding. Today, when the cattle are housed for the winter months, many are fed an especially formulated complete diet feed based on silage, grain and root crops. Regular checks ensure that essential components in the diet of the dairy herd are available from the feed.

The Weather

Weather plays an integral part in the working life of the farm. Tasks are determined by the daily weather and the timing of the seasons. Many innovations in farming are designed to reduce the effects of poor weather, and occasionally, drastic meteorological events contribute to change. The winter of 1947 was the worst for forty years. Thousands of sheep and cattle died, horses could not work, and tractors were sometimes the only vehicles that could get through the snowdrifts to isolated communities. Farming was badly affected, and the Agriculture Act was passed later that year to ease matters.

There was another severe winter in 1963, and in Somerset, milk collection and distribution was sometimes impossible. For two months the Somerset National Farmers Union, the Ministry, and the County Council organised the distribution of farm supplies. As a result the Milk Emergency Collection Scheme was established.

Land-Rover delivering feed to cattle in winter snow, Baltonsborough, 1960s.
(Courtesy of Mr W. Dunkerton)

Milking parlour at Lottisham Farm, 1937. (Photographer F. Higdon; 51/1999/10)

DAIRYING

Over the last hundred years dairying in Somerset has changed from a farm based activity to a major food industry. This has happened because of developments in dairy farming, milk processing and distribution, the adoption of new technologies, and the continuing demand for milk products. Dairy hygiene has been improved, and much of the manual labour associated with milking has been reduced.

1900s

One person could milk about ten cows by hand, sitting on a three legged milking stool and collecting the milk in pails.

1930s

The bucket plant allowed one person to milk about thirty cows a day, but most cows were still hand milked. In the late 1930s the first tandem milking parlours were introduced, powered by stationary engines.

1933

By the 1930s the system of quickly transporting milk by rail to fulfil urban demand was well established, and the Dairy Companies and Co-operative Societies were providing door-step delivery pasteurised milk. However, the economic depression and the unprofitability of other agricultural products induced more farmers to turn to milk, and prices subsequently fell. To stabilise the chaotic situation, the Government established the Milk Marketing Scheme in 1933, and the Milk Marketing Board negotiated milk prices until 1939.

1937-1938

The Milk Marketing Board introduced the Tuberculin Tested milk scheme, where producers were paid 2d. per gallon more for this grade of milk.

1939-1945

During the Second World War milk became one of the crucial issues. The shortage of other foods during the war made milk more important. The Ministry of Food promoted its nutritional value, and applied considerable effort to assure all-year-round supply. As a result consumption of liquid milk increased, despite a fall in production. This demand remained post-war, and when the Milk Marketing Board and the dairy trade took over again in 1954 annual milk production was up by 48% since 1939.

1946

Artificial insemination, pioneered by Sir John Hammond and Arthur Walton before the Second World War, was greeted with almost universal suspicion and resistance. To introduce it in Britain, the Milk Marketing Board undertook to provide AI facilities for farmers in England and Wales under the Agricultural (Artificial Insemination) Act of 1946.

1950s

Cooling milk discourages the multiplication of bacteria. In the 1930s and 1940s the surface cooler was widely used. The milk was cooled by passing it over a series of zig-zag metal tubes through which cold water was passed.

1960s

The first herringbone parlours were introduced. Bulk tanks, incorporating plate heat exchangers, started to be used in Somerset to collect and store milk in the dairy.

1970s

Refrigeration units running on off-peak electricity started to be used to cool the milk in bulk tanks.

1972

Britain joined the European Economic Community in 1972 and became subject to the Common Agricultural Policy with its complex arrangements for 'intervention' payments.

1974-1982

The Farm and Horticulture Development Scheme, operated by the Ministry of Agriculture, Fisheries and Food, was available to help agricultural businesses expand.

1984

By the 1980s with European production overall in surplus, supply was exceeding demand by about 30% and there was a 'butter mountain'. Dairy quotas were suddenly introduced in 1984, curtailing the expansion of the sector begun in the 1930s.

1990s

With an efficient system one person can milk 100 cows in an hour.

Interest Rates Taxes Insurance
Expenditure 1936-7

Date	Payee	Description	£	s	d
April 7	Gould & Swayne	½ years interest on £600 less tax	11	12	6
" "	Bath & Austin	Fire Insurance	1	5	6
May 5	Lillie	½ years interest on £300 less tax	5	1	3
" 30	Thomas	Employers Liability; Third Party Insurance	2	9	3
June 12	Mary	½ year Interest due June 12	15		
" 26	Shepton Council	Rates	6	4	10
Aug 21	Westminster B	Bank charges	3	3	6
Sept 8	Thomas	Water rate for Common		15	
" 18	Wm Haine	Water rate 61,000	4	2	
" 30	Pearce	Insurance of cottages		4	6
Oct 13	Gould Swayne	Interest ½ year on £600 less tax	11	8	9
" "	April Drewett	Tithe	1	15	1
Nov 25	Tabor	Interest ½ year due Nov 5 less tax	5	1	3
Dec 27	Shepton District Council	Rates	6	4	10
Jan 4	Mary	Interest due Dec 12	15		
" 12	Chemist	Pig powders		3	6
" 28	Tax Commission	Income tax & land tax	12	9	6
" "	Westminster Bank	charges	9	11	11
" 11	Haine	Water rate 45000 gall	3	4	4
Feb 7	Thomas	Water rate for common		15	
Oct	Drewett	Tithe	1	9	9
			117	2	3

Additions to Plant & Machinery

Date	Payee	Description	£	s	d
1936					
May 18	Bacon	20 standard Bars 22/6 Extractor 2.15.0	3	17	6
July 2	Burgess	Bee things		4	9
" 8	Mogg	3 horse Lister Engine	29	10	
" "	Mogg	1 cattle clipper	3	7	6
" 12	Alfa-Laval	Milking Machine	237	10	
" 21	Mathews	Shaft for Engine		18	
" 22	Pearce	Fence & Wheelbarrow body	2	11	8
Sept 1	Mogg	Milking bucket		9	
Oct 13	Drew Clark	Extension Ladder	2	15	
Jan 19	Wrights	Plunger Pumps	4	12	
Feb 16	Haine	Hive & Bars	2	1	3
			287	16	8

Lottisham Farm accounts. (51/1999/1)

1950s eight bay milking parlour built onto an older stone shed, Woodbridge Farm, Ubley, 1988. (P3379)

1950s milk cooler by Lister at Woodbridge Farm, 1988. (637/1990/3; P3376)

This page and opposite:
George Maidment at Plot Street Farm, West Bradley, using a bail to milk his herd of Shorthorns, 1960s. (P1417-P1420, P1422)

National Dairy Council advertisement in the *Daily Mail*, 1979. (SCMS)

David Patten milking at Stoke St Gregory, 1986. (S5526, S5527)

Milking parlour at Brent Farm, East Huntspill, 1988. (S5815)   Bulk tank at Brent Farm. (S5816)

Cow house at New Road Farm, East Huntspill, 1988. (S5805)

Grain hopper at New Road Farm, 1988. (S5812)

In the drive to increase milk yield, both in quantity and quality, the first half of the twentieth century saw the gradual shift from dual-purpose cattle to breeds specifically suited to beef or dairying. At the beginning of the century only 2% of the cow population were specialised dairy breeds, but by 1957 this had risen to 55%.

Selective breeding, made easier through artificial insemination (AI), has continued to increase yields. AI centres work with the breed societies to choose pedigree bulls of the highest quality, from whom semen is taken and frozen until it is needed. The practice enables a bull to sire over 20,000 calves a year, whereas by natural mating one bull would sire about 50 calves a year.

Milking machines

The first milking machines were developed in America in the nineteenth century, but they were painful for cattle and were difficult to keep clean. However the principles behind modern milking machines were established by the 1900s. In 1895 Dr Alexander Shield developed a 'pulsator' suction machine which drew milk from the udder with an on/off sucking action, and in 1902 Gillies developed a butyl rubber teat-cup which could be fitted more comfortably onto the udders.

Their introduction was not rapid. Only farmers with the largest herds could afford to install a milking machine, and pay the running and maintenance costs. In 1939 only 15% of cows in England and Wales were machine milked. Eventually with the arrival of mains electricity they became more acceptable.

The milking bail, a portable milking parlour, was developed in the 1920s by Arthur Hosier to milk cattle where they grazed on the Wiltshire Downs, some way from the farmsteads. The traditional pattern on many lowland Somerset dairy farms was to use outlying pasture for grazing, particularly in the Summer, and milking bails were ideally suited for this. With the vacuum pump powered by a stationary engine, the milking bail also had two small wheels so that it could be towed.

Higher Hill Farm, North Barrow

Above: 1965 Milking parlour and dairy at Higher Farm, North Barrow, last used in the early 1980s, and photographed in 1998. *Opposite:* The bulk tank is by Desco (Dairy Supply Co. Ltd, Park Royal, London). Much of the other equipment was supplied by Fulwood Ltd, and Somerset Milking Parlours Ltd. On the wall is a Milk Marketing Board calibration table for VAT. (S6720, P5155, P5160, P5181)

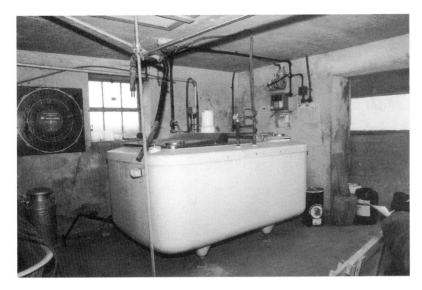

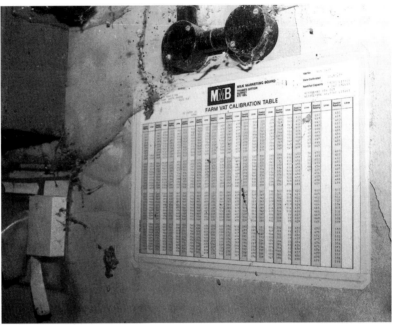

Somerset Milking Parlours

Throughout the nineteenth century there were many local manufacturers and suppliers providing dairy and cheesemaking equipment in Somerset, but there were far fewer during the twentieth century. The demand for milking bails in Somerset was met by Somerset Milking Parlours Ltd who first produced them at Walton, and then at Edington from 1969. Their engineering works also produced milking parlours and cubicles which were sold throughout the United Kingdom. The introduction of milk quotas in 1984 forced production to cease.

Dairy herd feeding inside a cow house made by Somerset Milking Parlours Ltd, 1969.
(Photographer Douglas Allen; Courtesy of Mr D. Gwilliam)

Manufacturing milking parlours, Somerset Milking Parlours Ltd, Edington, 1970.
(Photographer Douglas Allen; Courtesy of Mr D. Gwilliam)

Somerset 'Major Parlour', Somerset Milking Parlours Ltd, Edington, 1970.
(Photographer Douglas Allen; Courtesy of Mr D. Gwilliam)

Milking parlour with bulk tank, Somerset Milking Parlours Ltd, 1976.
(Photographer Douglas Allen; Courtesy of Mr D. Gwilliam)

Milking parlour with bulk tank by Desco, Somerset Milking Parlours Ltd, 1971.
(Photographer Douglas Allen; Courtesy of Mr D. Gwilliam)

*'Eventually we got a milking bail to go out into the fields, we bought
a tractor. We milked in the fields, moving from one to the other'.*

Norman Stevens, farmer, speaking of milking in Shapwick in the 1940s.

ARABLE

In Somerset before the Second World War the main factors which decided whether land was used for arable or livestock were the availability of drinking water and soil type. These considerations, together with the greater investment required for arable farming, tended to favour dairying in many parts of the county.

However, where arable farming is preferred, developments in land management, plant breeding and pest control have improved the returns, so that the average yield of grain is now at least double that in the 1900s. Wheat and barley are the predominant crops, rotated with oil seed rape and linseed, or root crops and maize grown as fodder.

1900s
Horse drawn reaper-binders and steam engine powered threshing machines were used for the harvest. Straw was built into ricks for storage, where it was thatched to protect it from the weather.

1914-1918
Active measures were introduced by the government to encourage corn growing. Pasture was ploughed up and livestock numbers reduced. Food rationing had to be introduced by the end of the First World War.

1940s
Tractors had replaced traction engines as the power source for the threshing drums, but horses pulling waggons from the fields loaded with sheaves of corn were commonplace. However, binders needed a lot of maintenance, and the business of drying and threshing the stooks of cut corn was very labour intensive.

Balers were still stationary machines designed to work behind a threshing drum.

1950s
The numbers of combine harvesters were increasing. Developed in America, they cut and threshed grain in one operation. The majority were towed by a tractor and powered either by a separate engine or from the tractor through a power take-off shaft. Self-propelled combines were expensive but could be operated by one person.

Twine-tying pick-up balers were introduced for hay and straw.

1970s
Fodder beet became a popular root crop.

Handling small bales became expensive. The alternative was to make large bales and mechanise the loading and stacking process.

1980s
Crops such as rape, linseed, and flax were increasingly grown, encouraged by attractive Common Agricultural Policy (CAP) payments, and maize became a popular source for silage.

The development of big round and square balers further reduced the labour needed.

1988
Set-aside, the system of CAP payments for taking land out of production to reduce surplus production, was introduced.

1990s
Genetically modified (GM) rapeseed and maize crops were trialed in various parts of the country. Although no GM trials had taken place in Somerset, public concern was mobilised over the potential hazards of GM organisms.

Harrowing, Wells area, c.1912. (Photographer A. Loynes; P337)

Drilling corn near Winscombe, c.1900. (Photographer Hole; 12/1994/453)

Drilling using a seed drill
with disc harrows c.1939.
(Photographer Dr
D. Chapman; P335)

The corn harvest, Luxborough, c.1900. (P392)

Harvesting wheat
with a reaper-binder,
Butleigh Wooton,
c.1920s. (P391)

Harvesting wheat with a reaper-binder, c.1930s. (P395)

1940s reaper-binder by John Deering at the Somerset Rural Life Museum, Glastonbury, 1970s.
(76.AR.212/1; P4148)

W. Knight (left), German prisoner of war (centre), and Mrs E. Knight using a threshing machine at Middle Burnham Farm, Edithmead, Burnham-on-Sea, c.1940.
(Courtesy of Mrs Drinkwater; 196/1987/7)

Threshing at Withycombe, c.1900. (P396)

Thatching a rick near Chard,
1940s. (P3805)

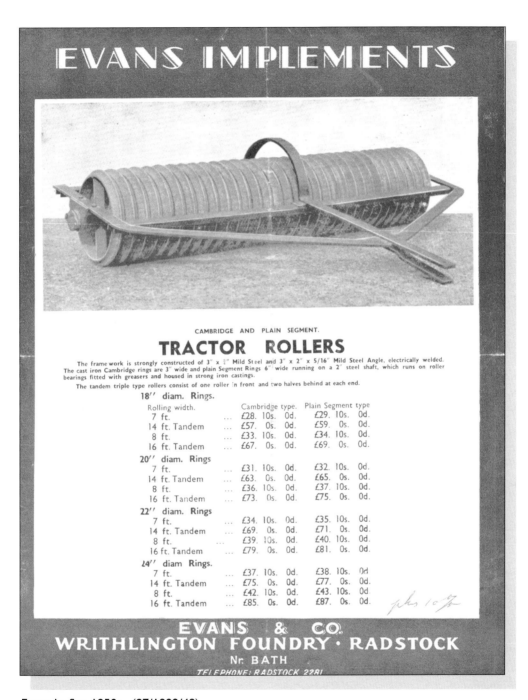

EVANS IMPLEMENTS

CAMBRIDGE AND PLAIN SEGMENT.
TRACTOR ROLLERS

The frame work is strongly constructed of 3″ x ¼″ Mild Steel and 3″ x 2″ x 5/16″ Mild Steel Angle, electrically welded. The cast iron Cambridge rings are 3″ wide and plain Segment Rings 6″ wide running on a 2″ steel shaft, which runs on roller bearings fitted with greasers and housed in strong iron castings.

The tandem triple type rollers consist of one roller in front and two halves behind at each end.

18″ diam. Rings.

Rolling width.	Cambridge type.	Plain Segment type
7 ft.	£28. 10s. 0d.	£29. 10s. 0d.
14 ft. Tandem	£57. 0s. 0d.	£59. 0s. 0d.
8 ft.	£33. 10s. 0d.	£34. 10s. 0d.
16 ft. Tandem	£67. 0s. 0d.	£69. 0s. 0d.

20″ diam. Rings

7 ft.	£31. 10s. 0d.	£32. 10s. 0d.
14 ft. Tandem	£63. 0s. 0d.	£65. 0s. 0d.
8 ft.	£36. 10s. 0d.	£37. 10s. 0d.
16 ft. Tandem	£73. 0s. 0d.	£75. 0s. 0d.

22″ diam. Rings

7 ft.	£34. 10s. 0d.	£35. 10s. 0d.
14 ft. Tandem	£69. 0s. 0d.	£71. 0s. 0d.
8 ft.	£39. 10s. 0d.	£40. 10s. 0d.
16 ft. Tandem	£79. 0s. 0d.	£81. 0s. 0d.

24″ diam. Rings.

7 ft.	£37. 10s. 0d.	£38. 10s. 0d
14 ft. Tandem	£75. 0s. 0d.	£77. 0s. 0d.
8 ft.	£42. 10s. 0d.	£43. 10s. 0d
16 ft. Tandem	£85. 0s. 0d.	£87. 0s. 0d.

plus 10%

EVANS & CO.
WRITHLINGTON FOUNDRY · RADSTOCK
Nr. BATH
TELEPHONE: RADSTOCK 2281

Evans leaflet, 1950s. (87/1999/48)

This page and opposite: International Harvester leaflets, 1950s. (87/1999/10,17,18)

TEMPLEWOOD
Range of modern Farm Machinery

GRASS DRYERS
GRAIN DRYERS
PROVENDER PRESSES
HAMMER MILLS
MEAL ELEVATORS
COMPOUND MIXERS

Templewood advertisement, 1950s. (87/1999/46)

Templewood
GRAIN DRYER

THE TEMPLEWOOD ENGINEERING Co. Ltd. have been fortunate in obtaining the licence to manufacture the Farm Grain Dryer designed by The International Harvester Company.

The dryer is portable, but far from sacrificing efficiency to gain mobility, this dryer can truly claim to be far ahead of all other grain dryers on the score of low running costs.

The machine is completely self-contained and can be operated in the field, moving from site to site with the combine, or can be set up equally well as a permanent installation in a barn. It requires no mains supplies and can be equipped with its own electric lighting if desired.

This dryer incorporates many novel features, including fully automatic controls and will evaporate approximately 107 lbs. water per hour which corresponds to 13½ cwt./hr. dried from 21 to 15% moisture content.

The fuel consumption is approximately 11 pints of gas oil per hour, whilst the power unit consumes about 10 pints of vaporising oil.

Grain enters the dryer at the top and flows downward past four longitudinal plenum chambers, which supply heat and drying air, and then emerges at the bottom through suitable metering augers. Drying air is drawn through the grain mass by a main exhaust fan, the air having previously been raised in temperature by passing through a heat exchanger; in addition, it is pre-heated by mixing with air which has passed through the radiator of the driving engine and also over the exhaust pipe. The exhaust system is arranged in such a way that grain entering the machine from the intake auger is pre-heated by radiation from the exhaust-pipe casing. The general dimensions of the machine, when ready for the road, are length 19 ft. 7 in., height 11 ft. 7 in. and width 7 ft. 5 in. Sheet-steel construction is used throughout, and the machine when full contains about 45 cwt. of grain, depth of grain being varied by the operator between 38 and 43 in. as required.

1950s Massey-Harris 735 combine harvester used at Manor Farm, Puckington near Ilminster, at the dispersal sale in 1999. (Photographer C. Soulsby)

Advertisement for self-propelled combine harvester in the *British Farmer*, 1965. (SCMS)

Loading small bales of straw, Hurlingpot Farm, 1983. (SCMS)

Massey-Ferguson 38 combine at Hurlingpot Farm, near Shepton Mallet, 1999. (SCMS)

Combining beans, 1988. (Photographer Miss P. Peacock)

Big bales of straw, 1988. (Photographer Miss P. Peacock)

Cartoon in the *Somerset Farmer*,
1985. (SCMS)

Spraying winter wheat with selective herbicide, near Shepton Mallet, 1999. (SCMS)

'The early combines had a bagging platform where one filled
the "West of England" hired sacks, which weighed two and a quarter
hundredweight if filled with wheat, tied them and then slid them
down a shoot. When the shoot was full with three or four sacks,
one pulled a cord and they slid down onto the ground.'

Allen Cotton, West Bradley

Glastonbury Genetics Group leaflet, 1998. (SCMS)

Genetic Engineering

This means taking genes from one plant or animal and artificially implanting them into a completely unrelated species. It's something which never happens in nature.

It can be very profitable for the big agrochemical companies.

For example soya beans can be made resistant to a weedkiller, allowing that weedkiller to be used much more widely.

But it has unpredictable effects on humans, farm animals, wildlife and the ecological processes which sustain all life.

Genes from fish have been put into tomatoes to give them a longer shelf life!

Damage which has *already been done* includes:

- Genes from Snowdrops, implanted in potatoes to make them resistant to aphids, have killed ladybirds - the natural predators of aphids.

- Soya beans had genes from brazil nuts put into them. People who are allegic to nuts who ate the soya suffered bad reactions. Soya is present in 60% of supermarket foods.

- Attempts to boost growth rates in sheep and pigs through gene technology have greatly increased their susceptibility to diseases, from diabetes to arthritis.

- In the USA 37 people may have been killed and 1500 permanently disabled by genetically modified bacteria used to produce the food supplement Tryptophan.

Governments and the EU are letting the genetic engineers have their own way.

But ordinary people can make a difference

1947 Agriculture Act

Traditionally farming was based on the relationship between landlord and tenant, but with the act the State became an active agent in agriculture. The act was in two parts, concerned with stability and efficiency.

Part 1 provided for guaranteed prices and markets based on an annual review held every February. Part 2 was concerned with the efficient standards of estate management. It became the duty of an owner of agricultural land to manage it efficiently.

The responsibility for maintaining reasonable standards of good estate management and animal husbandry rested with the County Agricultural Executive Committee, which had the power to give directions and impose supervision orders, enforceable through fines and, ultimately, dispossession.

Roots

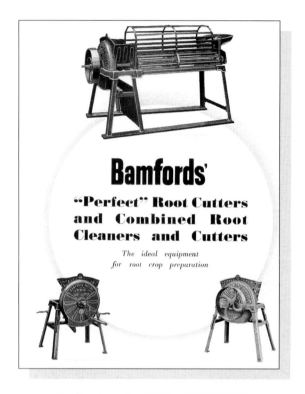

Bamfords leaflet, 1951. (87/1999/35)

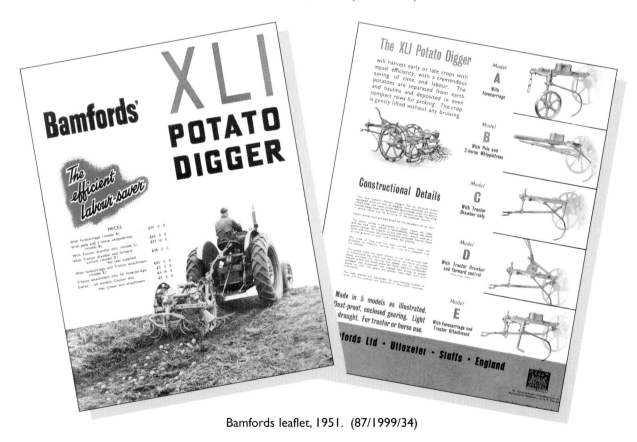

Bamfords leaflet, 1951. (87/1999/34)

Beet pulper by Harrison McGregor, used at Box Farm, Theale,
photographed at the dispersal sale in 1992. (P3591)

Flax

The rich loam soils to the south of the County are particularly suited to growing flax. Originally grown to produce linen cloth, webbing and twine from the stalks, it is now grown to produce linseed oil, which is extracted from the seeds.

Harvesting flax by members of the National Service Corps during the First World War, near Ilchester, 1917. (Courtesy of Dr D. Chapman; P289)

Spraying flax with herbicide near Shepton Mallet, 1999. (SCMS)

Ploughing near Wedmore, c.1914. (P347)

POWER

Up until the 1940s horses were the most widely used sources of power on the farm. Steam engines were used for ploughing and threshing, and of the few tractors available in the 1920s and 1930s towing implements from a draw bar was their main function. After the Second World War the demand for tractors increased and technological advances made them ever more powerful and adaptable. The biggest impact has been the reduction in labour needed on the farm.

1900-1930s

Steam engines were used for preparing the land and for threshing cereals. Although a few landowners owned their own machines, most were hired from steam engine contractors. Stationary engines started to replace the horse gear to power root slicing and chaff cutting machines.

1930s

The Fordson Standard was the most popular tractor of this period. First made in 1933, by 1939 three-quarters of all tractors used on British farms were Fordsons. As well as towing, a power take-off allowed machinery to be run from a belt pulley.

1945

The Fordson Major replaced the Standard in 1945. It had three forward gears and reverse. By the end of 1946 Fordsons accounted for four-fifths of tractors made in Britain.

1946

Ford's Standard Motor Company started to make the Ferguson TEA 20 in Coventry. Similar tractors had been made in America, and incorporated the Ferguson patented 'three point linkage'.

1948

There was considerable demand for new tractors, and Ford and Ferguson were joined by other manufacturers, including David Brown, Allis-Chalmers, Marshall, Massey-Harris and Nuffield. David Brown started making tractors in 1939, and many were used by the navy and air force during the Second World War. The Cropmaster was introduced in 1947, and the series was replaced in 1953 with six new tractors, for which sixty different implements were made.

1955

The first British-made International Harvester tractor, the B 250, appeared, although American-made International Harvester tractors had been used on British farms since the 1930s.

1960s

Most tractors had twin lever gearboxes with six or eight forward speeds and sophisticated power take-off systems. Only a few makes had weather cabs, which offered increased safety and comfort, and reduced noise levels.

An Aveling and Porter steam engine belonging to Squire Robert Neville Grenville with a cultivator in the foreground, Butleigh Court Estate, 1900s. (P500)

Robert Neville Grenville's steam ploughing team at Tuckrushing Field, Butleigh, 1930s. Stan Dimmock is on the plough and Reg Masters on the engine. (Courtesy of Mrs Masters; P2961)

Steam ploughing, West Somerset, c.1900. (Photographer Hole; 12/1994/254)

This page and opposite: Ploughing with a Fordson Major tractor, 1930s. The depth of ploughing is controlled by hand. (Photographer Dr D. Chapman; P339, P340)

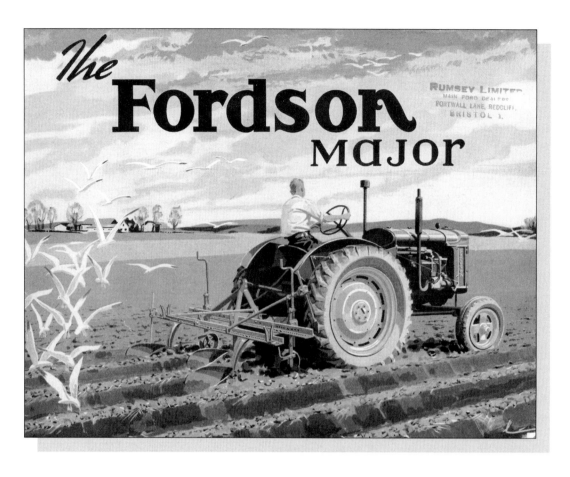

This page and opposite: Fordson leaflets, 1940s. (87/1999/1,4)

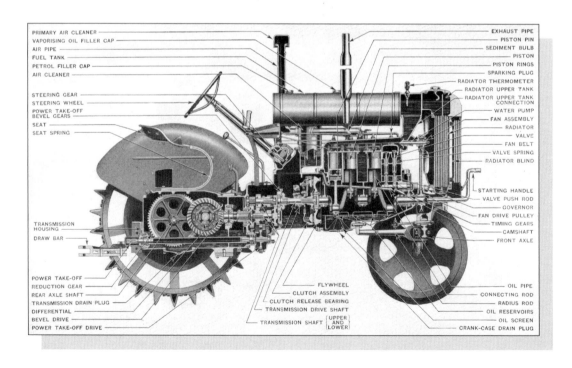

SAVE TIME AND MONEY

PLOUGHING

HARROWING

DRAG HARROWING

CULTIVATING

ROLLING

DISC HARROWING

SEED DRILLING

HAULING

Whatever the page on the Farm Calendar, there is work for a tractor to do and farmers everywhere have proved that the Fordson outworks all others. Owners of the latest Fordson Major are more than ever enthusiastic about its Yeoman qualities.

RIDGING

Below is shown the latest draw bar; a greatly improved component. It is readily adjustable horizontally and vertically. It ensures greater tractor stability and much easier handling of trailing implements.

DISTRIBUTING FERTILISER

HARVESTING

"COMBINE" HARVESTING

ALL THE YEAR ROUND

Fordson leaflets, 1940s. (87/1999/1,4)

Ferguson leaflet, 1950s. (87/1999/47)

Ferguson tractor in use at Steanbow Farm, Pilton, from an article in the *Land Girl*, 1944. (SCMS)

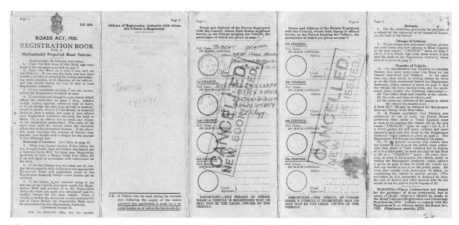

Case tractor registration document, West Town House farm, Baltonsborough, 1939. (SCMS)

THE Improved TYPE H.2 MOUNTED HARROW FRAME

THIS extended Harrow Frame is specially constructed to take full advantage of the Fordson Major's immense drawbar pull. Designed by Patrick & Wilkinson (Sales) Ltd., Belfast, in co-operation with Ford Motor Company Ltd., it combines lightness for easy handling, with an ample safety margin of strength to meet any abnormal stresses.

With this frame, which is fully mounted, harrowing can be done at much higher speeds. Harrows can also be cleaned in work, without manual assistance thus,

effecting a further saving in time and labour.

The frame, including the outriggers, is of solid drawn steel tubing, electrically welded throughout and braced fore and aft. It measures 8 ft. 3 in. with the outriggers closed and 16 ft. fully extended.

The levelling box and top 3-point linkage controls pitch of the implement justment from 26 to 30 saddle back harrows.

Ford Motor Company leaflet, 1950s.
(87/1999/5)

INTERCHANGEABLE HARROWS

Spring tooth, zig-zag and saddle back harrows are available for use with the Patrick & Wilkinson Harrow Frame.

THE SPRING TOOTH HARROW

has 15 spring tines set at 6 in. intervals and staggered to give ample clearance for rough work. The outriggers are removed when using this implement.

THE ZIG-ZAG HARROW

is made of flat section steel with 25, ⅜ in. tines on each of the 4 sections. The centre frame supports 2 sections and the outriggers one section each.

THE SADDLE BACK HARROW

is constructed of flat section steel welded throughout. Each section has 21, ⅜ in. square tines.

The Fordson Major

BRINGS POWER TO YOUR LAND

FORD MOTOR COMPANY LIMITED . . DAGENHAM . ESSEX

International Harvester leaflet, 1950s. (87/1999/14)

International Harvester leaflet, 1950s. (87/1999/14)

International Harvester leaflet, 1960s. (87/1999/6)

BAD HABITS

Working with unguarded P.T.O.'s

Cartoon in the *Somerset Farmer*, 1985. (SCMS)

Three point linkage

This had two advantages. The concept of a 'virtual hitch-point' allowed mechanical attachments to operate in conjunction with the tractor with much greater efficiency than if simply towed, and 'draft control' allowed the depth at which an implement worked in the soil to be automatically regulated by the effort needed to pull it. Ferguson patents on automatic hydraulic depth control systems lapsed in the late 1950s, when other manufacturers started to incorporate them in their designs.

Four-wheel drive

After the Second World War the Rover Company decided to build a utility vehicle at its 'shadow factory' at Solihull which it had been running for the Air Ministry since 1939. Perhaps one of the major influences behind this decision was the success of the Ferguson tractor being made under licence by the Standard Motor Company at their ex-shadow factory at Coventry.

The new vehicle would be built largely from 'Bermabright' aluminium alloy, to circumvent the steel shortages. The resulting Series 1 Land-Rover came into production in July 1948, priced £450. Originally intended as a 'stop-gap', it became a huge success, and by 1958 200,000 had been produced. Nowadays, most major vehicle manufacturing companies make all-wheel drive vehicles, for a wide range of markets.

Land-Rover at Short Breach Farm, Ashcott, 1950s. (Courtesy of Mrs E. Frampton; P5058)

PIGS

Pig production in Somerset pre-1950s was a 'cottage industry'. Small numbers of pigs were kept in pigsties or paddocks close to the farmhouse, and fed on swill and other waste products. Change was stimulated by the de-control of meat in 1954, together with technical advances abroad. Other innovations appeared at this time; mono-pitch buildings for farrowing, movable farrowing crates, and the outdoor pig-breeding system using corrugated iron arcs which are still such a feature on pig farms. By the close of the twentieth century the industry was in recession largely due to foreign competition.

1940s
The commonest breeds were the Large White, Large Black, Wessex Saddleback and the Berkshire.

1950s
The Danish Landrace breed became strongly established, and the first large fattening piggeries were built, based on a Danish design. They had central feeding passages and outside dunging passages which could be scraped clean by tractor.

Producers began to specialise in different types of pig carcases. The large White, Welsh and Landrace were particularly suited for bacon, and Wessex for outdoor production.

The Unilever company, Wall's Meat, was particularly innovative. They introduced a system which offered contracts for 240lb liveweight pigs, using different parts of the pig for a complete range of products, with the large carcase giving low unit costs of production.

1954
End of rationing and the de-control of meat.

1960s
Wall's Meat introduced the first commercial AI service, and the world's first hybrid breeding programme, which aimed to offer prolific hybrid females to contractors to produce cheap weaners which fattened faster.

1970s
Selective breeding for better feed conversion and reduced backfat continued in the 1970s, as did further intensification. The weaning age came down to three weeks, made possible by the development of specialist controlled environment buildings, and feeds containing cooked cereals and milk powders.

1980s
Breeding companies have introduced Hampshire and Duroc blood into the stock.

1990s
Cheaper production costs abroad combined with the strength of the pound make British Pigs for home consumption and export uncompetitive.

Arthur Pope's piglets, Henley Cottage, Butleigh, 1978. (SCMS)

Saddleback sow at Henley Cottage, 1978. (P5009)

Farmer & Stock-Breeder advertisement, 1953. (SCMS)

Farmer & Stock-Breeder advertisement, 1953. (SCMS)

Above and opposite page: Pigs near Charterhouse, Mendip, 2000. (SCMS)

Poultry House. W. & A. Edgell Ltd catalogue, 1935. (160/1992/1)

POULTRY

Up until the 1930s poultry simply augmented a farm's income. Nearly all poultry were free range, and there was no division between poultry meat and egg production. By the end of the twentieth century both sectors have become increasingly specialised and mechanised. The decline of the traditional British breakfast in favour of cereals, and public concern over health issues, have all contributed to a drop in consumption.

1930s

The first systems for specialised housing were centred around urban areas, where flocks were kept in uninsulated cabins with access to fields. Before 1939 approximately one third of eggs were imported.

1939

Poultry food was rationed between 1939 and 1954. Trade in eggs and poultry was mainly local.

1945

A deep litter system was developed using straw as litter and insulation and colony nest boxes on the ground, housing 50 to 200 birds bought as day old chicks and reared under paraffin heated brooders.

1950s

Cross breeding removed the traditional breeds from commercial use, and introduced hybrids based on the White Leghorn which produced white eggs. When public demand grew for brown eggs, Rhode Island Red and American New Hampshire strains were used.

1959

The Broiler system of poultry meat production was introduced from the USA. Several thousand chicks were housed in insulated buildings with controlled ventilation, and brooded by hot water, electricity or gas.

This intensification was only possible with adequate disease control. Vaccines were applied regularly to prevent fowl paralysis (Mareks), infectious bronchitis, fowl pest, egg drop syndrome and epidemic tremors. The use of antibiotics became widespread to control bacterial diseases.

1960s

The obstacles to intensification of the egg industry, the removal of manure and effective control of the environment, were overcome by adopting the Californian cage system. This allowed droppings to fall straight into a pit, with air drawn over the manure and away from the house.

1980s

The awareness of the cholesterol in eggs as a risk factor for heart disease, and public concern over the extent of Salmonella in eggs became issues.

Government influence on the egg industry has been significant. After the Second World War the Egg Marketing Board branded its product with a little lion. The Eggs Authority came after the Egg Marketing Board. This body was empowered to raise a levy for promotional and research activities. Currently the lion is being re-introduced to market British eggs.

HEBDITCH'S DEEP LITTER POULTRY HOUSES.

Equally suitable for Brooder or Intensive methods. Made in sections, and can be extended to any length. Perfect ventilation. Wide sliding door at each end. Built of high-class material and all timber pickled.

Send for full particulars of Deep Litter Houses and Appliances and all Poultry Equipment.

Pig Houses, Sheds, Garages and Greenhouses supplied. *Folder free.*

HARRY HEBDITCH, LTD. (Dept. F. & S.), MARTOCK, SOMT. 'Phone: Martock 2200

Farmer & Stock-Breeder advertisement, 1953. (SCMS)

---

48   S. YOUNG & SONS (MISTERTON) LTD.

EGG TESTER

Thoroughly reliable and nothing to get out of order. At a turn of the switch the whole contents of the eggs are visible.

Enamel finished ; top padded with black substance for better illumination of the egg.

Complete with battery. 12/6 Post free.

THE AMAZING "SMALLHOLDER" EGG GRADER

Here is an Egg Grader as accurate and fast as elaborate machines which cost fifty times the price. No Poultry Farmer, Smallholder, or Backyarder should be without it.

Grades 1,500—1,800 per hour.

So simple—a child can use it.

No spring—nothing to get out of order.

All four grades at a glance.

LARGE are marked "FIRST" and are $2\frac{3}{16}$ oz. upwards.

STANDARD are marked "SECOND" and are $1\frac{7}{8}$ oz. to $2\frac{3}{16}$ oz.

MEDIUM are marked "THIRD" and are $1\frac{5}{8}$ oz. to $1\frac{7}{8}$ oz.

SMALL do not lift the centre pin and are below $1\frac{5}{8}$ oz.

Eggs are not Potatoes !

The above may seem to be an unnecessary remark to make, but supposing potatoes had to be weight graded. You could simply throw them on to a grading machine.

Eggs are altogether a different proposition.

Eggs being fragile have to be handled separately, even by big packing stations, and must be placed by Hand on to any machine that does grading, and removed by Hand from such a machine. This means that because you cannot simply throw them on, that the speed depends upon the rate of individual handling.

With this remarkable grader, as soon as an egg is placed upon it, the grade is instantly registered. Thus grading speeds per person can approximately equal the speed attained by the most expensive of machines, and the accuracy is very high indeed. Price **20/-**.

THE "SUPER SAFETY" CHICK BOX FOR DAY OLDS

Prevent Suffocation, Give Perfect Protection and Ensures Safe Arrival

To hold 12's, **160/-** gross ; Dozen Lots, **1/6** each. To hold 25's, **190/-** gross ; Dozen Lots, **1/9** each. To hold 50's, **330/-** gross ; Dozen Lots, **2/9** each. .050 Kraft Lined Container Board. Loose Lid. Stock Printed Extra   Supplied complete with Circluts.

S. Young & Sons (Misterton) Ltd, 1957 catalogue. (161/1992/80)

Suprema

The Somerset Poultry Marketing Association was founded at Eastfields Farm, Edington in 1936 by the poultry farmer Lieutenant Colonel Roe as a co-operative society with the brand name 'SUPREMA'. Eggs were collected from farms across Somerset in vans, and tested, graded, cleaned and packed for distribution by road and rail.

At its peak over 80 people worked at the egg packing station, which was replaced by a new building in 1951 incorporating cold storage units. However in 1969 Suprema was forced to merge with a packing station in Exeter and the site was sold.

Mucking out a poultry house at Eastfields Farm, Edington, 1940s. The egg packing station is in the distance to the left. Fred Gillard, the foreman, stands with the horse. (Courtesy of Mrs I. Panter)

Moving a fold from one field to
another, Eastfields Farm, 1940s.
(Courtesy of Mrs I. Panter)

The new egg packing station
at Eastfields Farm, 1950s.
(Courtesy of Mrs I. Panter)

Inside the new egg
packing station, 1969.
(Photographer Douglas Allen;
Courtesy of Mr D. Gwilliam)

SHEEP

Prior to the Second World War sheep management in Somerset had altered little for 150 years. Post-war changes adversely affected sheep farming. New fertilisers and pesticides made the Norfolk rotation of crops no longer so necessary, and cash crops of potatoes and sugar beet replaced the turnip. Broader political and economic factors were unfavourable, and there was a change in public taste away from mutton. Circumstances changed again in the 1970s and there was some expansion. However in recent years support for hill farming has reduced, jeopardising the economy and land management of upland areas such as Exmoor.

1947

The 1947 Agriculture Act sought to give assured prices to producers linked to subsidised prices to consumers. Sheep were included in this policy, and as a consequence New Zealand lamb was to remain the central issue determining the size of the British sheep industry for the next twenty-five years. British lamb was seen as a complement to the plentiful supplies of New Zealand lamb, and as a result the sector remained virtually static.

1950s

The introduction of electric fencing made sheep management significantly easier, particularly on lowland farms.

1970s

In-wintering is the technique which has allowed the intensification of sheep keeping on lowland farms. Begun in the 1970s, keeping sheep in winter housing and indoor lambing has improved the overall stocking and lambing rates to the extent that lamb production became competitive with arable cropping.

1973

When the UK entered the European Economic Community in 1973 an import tariff on New Zealand lamb combined with higher prices within the Community resulted in expansion.

1980s

On upland farms increased output has been due to selective breeding improvements, and better hill fencing. The advent of the quad bike has made it easier for the sheep farmer to check and move sheep flocks.

1990s

The pound has become relatively strong against the euro in which Common Agricultural Policy intervention prices are paid, making these payments worth less.

This page and opposite: Sheep shearing in Somerset, c.1939.
(Photographer Dr D. Chapman; P750, P797, P798)

Bill Webb, shepherd at Manor Farm, Curry Rivel, with a flock of Dorset Down sheep, c.1966.
(Courtesy of Mr A. Lang; 139/144)

John Small, farmer, on a quad bike at Charterhouse Warren Farm, near Priddy, 1990s.
(Courtesy of Mendip Hills AONB Service)

BEEF

In Somerset in the 1930s most farms reared some beef cattle, either as a by-product of the dairy herd, or to provide manure for the arable farm. Seventy years later farms are more specialised. A beef producing farm may do nothing else. Traditional breeds like the Shorthorn and the Devon Red have been replaced by breeds from the Continent such as the Charolais and the Simmental.

Beef

1930s

Steers were not sold for slaughter until they were much heavier than now, and many would be over three years old. The sale price for a steer weighing about 15cwt was £25.00. Heifers were not bred from until they were nearly three years of age, much later than now.

With the winter came hard manual tasks. Piped water was a rarity. Water in the summer was either from ponds or ditches, but in the winter it had to be pumped by hand from shallow wells. Winter feeding was also hard work. Hay and straw had to be cut off in squares from the ricks by hand, and carried by fork. Mangolds were put through a hand-turned chopper and mixed with diced sugar beet pulp and chaff or chopped straw.

Protein was provided by linseed and cotton cake, both industrial by-products, which arrived on the farm in slabs and were put through a hand operated cake breaker. Sugar beet pulp, from the sugar industry, was the only thing coming onto the farm in sacks.

1940s

The majority of cattle were sold at cattle markets in the local town. There were also calf markets throughout Somerset where dairy farmers sold their surplus stock. A well managed dairy herd need only breed replacements from its own cows, and with the advent of artificial insemination, the remaining, the low-yielders, could be put to Angus, Galloway or Hereford bulls, and the resultant calves contribute to the beef supply and save imports.

1970s

The market demand for smaller joints with lower fat content was met by breeding for earlier maturity. The traditional breeds were known for their ability to fatten on grass, but the earlier maturing continental breeds could be exploited with the coming of concentrated feed.

1990s

With improvements in mechanical handling, the introduction of bales for hay, straw, and silage, together with the elimination of processing roots, labour on a beef breeding farm was considerably less than in the 1930s.

John Crang at Cary Fitzpaine Farm, Charleton Mackrell, with his herd of Devon Red cattle, 1929. (P203)

Harry Snook and son Harold of Durborough Farm, Nether Stowey, with homebred Shorthorn steers. Bridgwater Christmas Fatstock Show, 1933. (P3771)

Harry and Harold Snook with a Devon Red cow, Bridgwater Christmas Fatstock Show, 1937. (Photographer F. Wilkins; P3770)

MID-SOMERSET AGRICULTURAL SHOW,
SHEPTON MALLET.
Tuesday, September 7th, 1937.

JOHN ROBINSON & Co., Ltd.
(BRANCH OF THE BRITISH OIL & CAKE MILLS, LTD.) BRISTOL.

Hope to have the pleasure of seeing
you at their

STAND.

August, 1937.
J. C. WALL.

Feed suppliers card, 1937. (51/1999/5)

Cattle judging guide, The Farmer Publications, 1950s. (87/1999/50)

Bamfords leaflet, 1951. (81/1999/45)

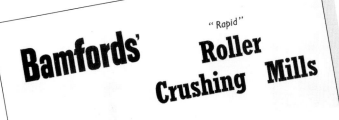

"Rapid"

Bamfords' Roller Crushing Mills

Strongly constructed.

*

Equipped with large smooth adjustable crushing rollers.

*

Simple, easily regulated feed arrangement.

DC Roller Mill fitted with Grinding Attachment

Specially suitable for crushing oats, rye, malt, barley, linseed, etc.

Bamfords leaflet, 1951. (87/1999/39)

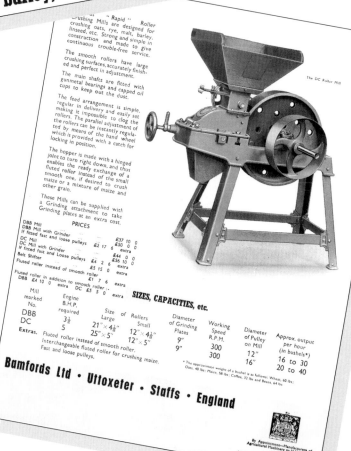

Bamfords' "Rapid" Roller Crushing Mills are designed for crushing oats, rye, malt, barley, linseed, etc. Strong and simple in construction and made to give continuous trouble-free service.

The smooth rollers have large crushing surfaces, accurately finished and perfect in adjustment.

The main shafts are fitted with gunmetal bearings and capped oil cups to keep out the dust.

The feed arrangement is simple, regular in delivery and easily set making it impossible to clog the rollers. The parallel adjustment of the rollers can be instantly regulated by means of the hand wheel which is provided with a catch for locking in position.

The hopper is made with a hinged joint to turn right down, and thus enables the ready exchange of a fluted roller instead of the small smooth one, if desired to crush maize or a mixture of maize and other grain.

These Mills can be supplied with a Grinding attachment to take Grinding plates at an extra cost.

The DC Roller Mill

PRICES

DBB Mill	£37 10 0	
DBB Mill with Grinder	£50 0 0	
If fitted fast and loose pulleys	£2 17 6	extra
DC Mill	£44 0 0	
DC Mill with Grinder	£56 10 0	
If fitted fast and Loose pulleys	£4 2 6	extra
Belt Shifter	£5 15 0	
Fluted roller instead of smooth roller	£1 7 6	extra
Fluted roller in addition to smooth roller :-		
DBB £4 10 0 extra DC £5 5 0	extra	

SIZES, CAPACITIES, etc.

Mill marked No.	Engine B.H.P. required	Size of Rollers Large	Small	Diameter of Grinding Plates	Working Speed R.P.M.	Diameter of Pulley on Mill	Approx. output per hour (in bushels*)
DBB	3½	21" × 4⅛"	12" × 4⅛"	9"	300	12"	16 to 30
DC	5	25" × 5"	12" × 5"	9"	300	16"	20 to 40

Extras. Fluted roller instead of smooth roller. Interchangeable fluted roller for crushing maize. Fast and loose pulleys.

* The approximate weight of a bushel is as follows: Wheat, 60 lbs; Oats, 40 lbs; Maize, 58 lbs; Coffee, 32 lbs and Beans, 64 lbs.

Bamfords Ltd · Uttoxeter · Staffs · England

By Appointment—Manufacturers of Agricultural Machinery to H.M. The King

List No. 2140. June, 1951. Printed in England

Bamfords leaflet, 1951. (87/1999/36)

Bamfords "Rapid" HAMMER MILL

Will deal with practically all kinds of material in dry condition, giving a uniform sample of any desired grade according to the screen used

easy accessibility to all the working parts

This Mill is strongly built of the best materials to ensure long life and satisfactory performance under exacting conditions.

The body is of high-duty cast iron, with the **top half hinged to allow inspection or adjustment of the working parts.**

The Fan casing is separate from the Mill, but is secured thereto by studs passing through circular lugs on the Mill body.

The Screen is of large area and the powerful Fan draws the ground material through the Screen and elevates it to a Cyclone having two outlets, controlled by a flap, so that one bag can be changed whilst the other is being filled.

The Hammers are of the swinging type, and are reversible, thus giving **four stepped cutting edges, two at each end.**

The Mill has 24 Hammers arranged in 8 rows on a Rotor mounted on the Main Shaft, the latter running in self-aligning **Ball Bearings in independent housings.**

The Feed Hopper is adjustable in height and has two adjustable slides to regulate the feed to the Mill.

The end of the Feed Hopper is removable for feeding straw or similar long material into the Mill.

Two Screens are supplied with the Mill which, unless otherwise ordered, will be supplied ⅛" and ¼". A large range of other sizes of Screens is available if specially ordered.

CAPACITIES, DIMENSIONS, ETC.

Normal speed of Mill : 1,800 to 2,000 r.p.m.

Normal b.h.p. required : 18 to 20 (higher power up to 30 b.h.p. can be used giving increased output).

Pulley on Mill : 5″ diameter ; 8″ face ; 1¹⁵⁄₁₆″ bore.

Screen : Diameter 29¼″ ; Width 10¼″ ; Area 465 sq. ins.

Hammers : No. 24 : size 8″ × 2″ × ⅜″.

Fan : 6 blades ; 24″ diameter.

Overall dimensions (with Cyclone) : Length 7-ft. ; Width 8-ft. : Height 7-ft. 3-in.

APPROXIMATE OUTPUT IN LBS. PER HOUR

The output of Hammer Mills depends on varying factors such as the B.H.P. used, the mesh of the sieve, and the moisture content of the material, so that the figures given below are only a rough guide as to the performance of the Mill.

OATS (⅛″ Screen) 1800 lbs. at 20 B.H.P. 2000 lbs. at 30 B.H.P.

BARLEY (⅛″ Screen) 2400 lbs. at 20 B.H.P. 2700 lbs. at 30 B.H.P.

Price - - £106 - 0 - 0

Bamfords Ltd · Uttoxeter · Staffs · England

By Appointment — Manufacturers of Agricultural Machinery to H.M. The King

List No. 2132. April, 1951. Printed in Engla[nd]

Preparing an Aberdeen Angus bull, Dunster Show, 1989. (Photographer Miss P. Peacock)

Weaning

Traditionally, calves were suckled by their mothers for a number of weeks before being weaned. Nowadays only about four days are allowed, although a calf is still fed on its mother's milk, and perhaps later dried milk, through a feeding device.

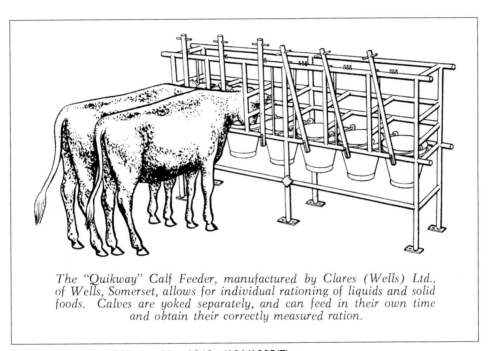

The "Quikway" Calf Feeder, manufactured by Clares (Wells) Ltd., of Wells, Somerset, allows for individual rationing of liquids and solid foods. Calves are yoked separately, and can feed in their own time and obtain their correctly measured ration.

British Oil & Cake Mills booklet, 1960. (101/1995/7)

A veal calf rearing house, near Shepton Mallet. From an article in *Sheldons Quarterly Review*, 1962. (141/1993/2)

BSE

1970s

Although all the circumstances are not yet fully understood, the cattle disease Bovine Spongiform Encephalopathy (BSE) is caused by a misshaped version of a protein called a prion, the normal version of which is found naturally in nervous tissue. A similar condition exists in sheep called scrapie. The rogue prion may be the result of a spontaneous mutation in cattle which was then spread by the practice of including infected tissue in cattle feed. Another factor may have been the reduction of the operating temperatures of rendering plants in the 1970s. This was permitted by a government directive to reduce costs after oil price rises. Previously, rogue prions might have been destroyed by the higher temperatures.

1980s

The condition became primarily established in the dairy herds. Because surplus cattle from the dairy herds enter the human food chain infected offal and nervous tissue is implicated in causing the human version, Variant Creutzfeldt-Jakob Disease (V-CJD). The use of protein from sheep, cattle and deer in cattle feed was banned in 1988.

1990s

Vigorous schemes were put in place to ensure that meat comes from BSE free cattle. However, the disease has caused a major crisis in British farming.

MAFF **BOVINE SPONGIFORM ENCEPHALOPATHY (BSE)**

Advisory notes for farmers

BSE became a notifiable disease on June 21, 1988. Whenever you or your veterinary surgeon suspect BSE in one of your cattle, you must therefore report the fact to your local Divisional Veterinary Officer (DVO). These notes briefly outline procedures that will be followed by the Ministry's officers, and give general guidance on various aspects of the disease.

BACKGROUND

BSE was first recognised in November 1986, and although seen mainly in dairy breeds, can affect all breeds farmed in Britain.

Clinical symptoms are very similar to those seen in Scrapie in sheep. In fact, Scrapie infected sheep are thought to be the origin of BSE, not by direct contact on the farm, but most probably through the feeding of contaminated meat-and-bone meal. Since then, BSE infected material will also have passed through the rendering system, allowing recycling of the disease to cattle.

The use of ruminant protein (ie from animals such as sheep, cattle, and deer) in ruminant diets was banned in July 1988 to cut off this source of transmission.

The majority of affected cattle will have been infected as calves, with the first infections most probably occurring in 1981 or 1982. Although the incubation period seems to range from two and a half to eight years, most animals are four to five years of age when they become affected. BSE has not been confirmed in animals under 22 months of age.

BSE was made notifiable on June 21, 1988. Anybody who suspects that his cattle are suffering from it must report it to the Ministry.

Following the advice of an expert committee set up specifically to look at the evidence, a slaughter with compensation policy was introduced on 8 August, 1988. This ensured that all carcases of suspect cattle were prevented from being sold for human consumption. In addition, the sale or supply of milk from BSE suspects was later banned. Both were decisions of extreme caution, since there is no evidence that BSE is infectious to man.

Compensation for infected cattle was increased on 14 February 1990, when the extent of the disease had become clearer.

SYMPTOMS

Most BSE cases show gradual development of symptoms over a period of several weeks, or even months, but a small number can deteriorate very rapidly. It should be emphasised that the symptoms summarised overleaf reflect changes in the individual animals and would not be expected to appear at under two years of age. Most suspects show several of the listed symptoms. Other diseases cause similar symptoms. If you have any doubt about the diagnosis, you should therefore consult your veterinary surgeon.

Stress appears to cause more rapid development of clinical signs in some animals, particularly when brought in before calving, or if transported.

1

MAFF leaflet, 1990. (SCMS)

WORK WEAR

Work wear in agriculture developed during the twentieth century into a specialised form of protective clothing. These advances were partly stimulated by the availability of new materials, but the greatest influence came from new legislation in 1974 which put pressure on farmers to provide special clothing and equipment to protect their employees.

1900s
Most farm workers made do with old jackets, waistcoats, and trousers which they tucked into their boots. Gloves and knee pads were used for special tasks like hedging, ditching, and thatching. Women doing farm work wore dresses, or blouses with an apron or a sleeveless overall.

1930s
Rubber boots became the usual footwear for farm workers. Farmers would still wear their boots and gaiters to market but rubber boots were a significant improvement on the farm.

1940s
The Women's Land Army was re-established and issued with special clothing. Their uniforms consisted of a hat, jumpers, shirts, ties, knee-breeches, woollen stockings, boots, Wellington boots and denim dungarees. After the Second World War many workers wore Army Surplus garments.

1974
The Health and Safety at Work Act came into force. This piece of legislation played a key role in the development of protective clothing by placing duties on companies and individuals to ensure that the work place was safe.

1980s
A number of regulations were introduced concerning the use of poisonous substances which again put pressure on farmers to protect their employees from hazards such as handling weed killers and pesticides. These include the 1984 Poisonous Substances in Agriculture Regulations, and the 1988 Control of Substances Hazardous to Health (COSHH) Regulations.

In 1989 the Noise at Work Regulations were introduced. These aimed to reduce hearing damage caused by loud noise. Employers had a duty to provide ear protectors if noise levels could not be reduced to a safe level.

1990s
This decade witnessed the introduction of a series of health and safety regulations implementing European Community directives. The 1992 Personal Protective Equipment (PPE) at Work Regulations most dramatically affected work wear. These regulations emphasise the supply and use of PPE whenever there are risks to health and safety that cannot be controlled in other ways.

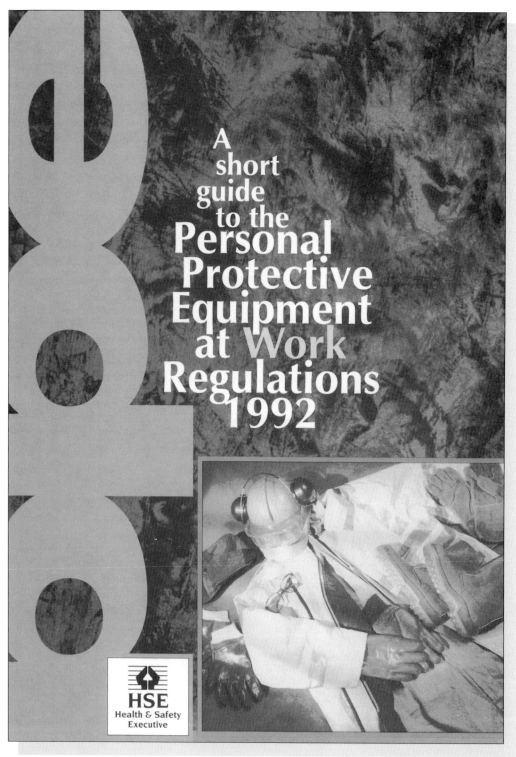

HSE Leaflet, 1994.

Clares of Wells

The Wells-based firm Clares played a key role in the development of work wear and protective clothing, and became one of Europe's largest manufacturers. In 1939 the Board of Trade decreed that Clares Covernee should become the one and only standard milking overall. In the 1950s the company advertised its Claramac, designed for the agricultural community. This garment made use of the relatively new material polyvinyl chloride (PVC).

Trade stand, Clares of Wells, 1950s.
(Courtesy of Clares Dickies Ltd)

Above: Argyll boot display by Clares Carlton Ltd, 1960s. (Courtesy of Clares Dickies Ltd)

Right: Display of work wear by Clares of Wells, 1970s. (Courtesy of Clares Dickies Ltd)

Bamfords leaflet, 1951. (87/1999/22)

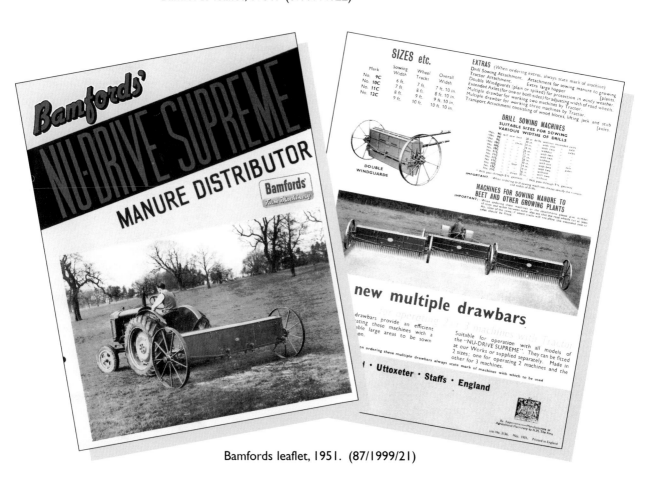

Bamfords leaflet, 1951. (87/1999/21)

FERTILITY

At the start of the twentieth century the traditional methods of crop rotation together with the application of lime, farmyard manure, and animal by-products, were used to maintain soil fertility. By the 1930s chemical fertilisers were also widely used. Their development has continued, but today, a high cost combined with the recognition that excess nitrates are an environmental hazard, has resulted in their restricted use.

1930s

The nature of the main elements depleted in the soil by agriculture were well known, and ammonium sulphate, 'superphosphate', and potassium sulphate were all being manufactured as farm fertilisers to replace the nitrogen, phosphorous, and potassium needed for vigorous growth of crops.

1950s

Compound fertilisers of ready-made mixtures came onto the market, some designed for specific crops.

1960s

The most usual source of nitrogen, ammonium sulphate, was a by-product of the coal gas industry, but with the introduction of natural gas in the 1960s it was no longer made. As an alternative, an industrial method of manufacturing ammonium nitrate, such as 'Nitram', was developed. Ammonia gas is mixed with hot nitric acid and the solution sprayed into the top of a tower. The droplets cool to form pellets. Fertilisers were relatively cheap and increased production more than paid for their cost.

1970s & 1980s

Increases in the price of natural gas, the raw material for the manufacture of ammonia, put up the price of artificial fertilisers. This, combined with the recognition of excess nitrates as an environmental hazard, has resulted in their more careful and timely application today.

PRICES OF
PROCTOR'S COMPLETE FERTILISERS
ON RAIL AT WORKS.

MANGOLD AND SUGAR BEET.
Nitrogen 3%   Sol. Phos. 16%
Potash 6%
Credit Price .. **£6 10 0** per ton.
Less 15/- per ton cash discount.
Apply 6 cwt. per acre for Mangolds.
8 „ „ for Beet.

SWEDE, TURNIP AND GENERAL ROOT CROPS.
Nitrogen 1½%   Sol. Phos. 16%
Potash 2%
Credit Price .. **£5 5 0** per ton.
Less 15/- per ton cash discount.
Apply 4 to 5 cwt. for Swedes and Turnips.
6 to 8 „ for Mangolds.

SPECIAL POTATO.
Nitrogen 3%   Sol. Phos. 16%
Potash 8%
Credit Price .. **£6 17 6** per ton.
Less 15/- per ton cash discount.
Apply 6 to 8 cwt. per acre.

No. 1—CORN, BARLEY AND OAT.
Nitrogen 3%   Sol. Phos. 16%
Potash 5%
Credit Price .. **£6 7 6** per ton.
Less 15/- per ton cash discount.
Apply 3 cwt. per acre.

No. 2—CORN, BARLEY AND OAT.
Nitrogen 1½%   Sol. Phos. 16%
Potash 5%
Credit Price .. **£5 17 6** per ton.
Less 15/- per ton cash discount.
Apply 3 cwt. per acre.

GRASS AND CLOVER.
Nitrogen 1½%   Sol. Phos. 10%
Insol. Phos. 10%   Potash 2%
Credit Price .. **£5 2 6** per ton.
Less 15/- per ton cash discount.
Apply 5 cwt. per acre.

Lowest Current Market Price, according to quantity, will be quoted for on request.

Superphosphate 30%
XXX Super 35%
Potassic Superphosphate
Compound Dissolved Bone
North African Phosphate
Potassic Mineral Phosphate 40 and 10
„ „ „ 50 and 5
Basic Slag (all grades)
Sulphate of Ammonia
Nitrate of Soda
Nitro-Chalk
Kainit 14%
Potash Salts 30%
Muriate of Potash 80%
Sulphate of Potash 90%
English Bone Meal
Steamed Bone Flour
Etc., etc.

We supply all kinds of Fertilisers.

Proctor's price list, 1930s. (14/1986)

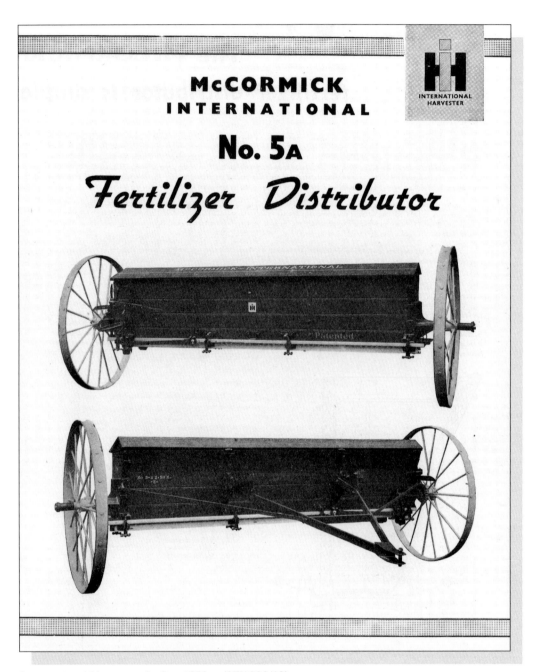

International Harvester leaflet, 1950s. (87/1999/12)

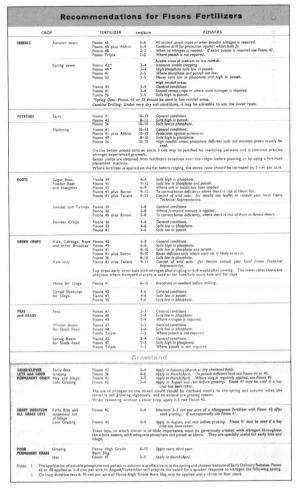

Fisons price list, 1960s. (41/1993/4)

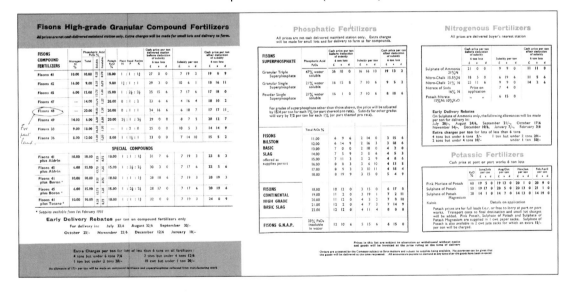

Ammonium nitrate has the advantage of containing more nitrogen than ammonium sulphate, but it has the disadvantage of remaining soluble in the soil. Applications of nitrogen in excess of that which a crop can take up can result in nitrates being washed into watercourses where they can cause 'algal blooms'. Eventually, unacceptably high levels of nitrates can end up in drinking water.

Watering young apple trees, 1930s. (P332)

ORCHARDS

Cider apple orchards are an essential element of Somerset's landscape. As well as providing a crop, livestock grazed under the 'standard' trees. The orchards have also been in decline during most of the twentieth century, as their economic significance has waned. However in recent years, with greater importance placed on regional distinctiveness, and to be less dependent on imported apple juice, they are now recognised as a valuable resource.

1940s
Cider 'truck', the giving of cider as part of a farm-worker's wages, had been made illegal in 1887, but it was still a significant factor in the lives of farm-workers. With the increased mechanisation of farming and the coming of more regulated working practices, cider became less important.

1950s
Dessert fruit began to replace cider varieties, but in 1958 there were still 18,000 acres of cider orchards.

1973
Farmhouse cider had become unfashionable as the public demanded a more standardised product. Larger manufacturers were able to import apple concentrate, and the acreage had declined to 2400 acres.

1980s
Although there were less orchards, the productivity had increased considerably. This was due to greater care, and the introduction of new varieties and practices. Bush trees allow the crop to be machine-picked without the use of casual labour. They can be planted more closely than 'standard' trees, which have a six foot trunk before the branches form.

1990s
Nationally, cider became a trendy drink, particularly with young women. In the five years since 1989 the market doubled.

Recently larger cider-makers like Matthew Clark at Shepton Mallet have encouraged the planting of Somerset orchards to reduce their dependence on imported European apple concentrate. They are signing thirty-year agreements to buy the fruit at market prices.

Spraying apple trees, probably with tar oil winter wash against the over-wintering eggs of various pests, 1930s. (Photographer A. Turner; 60/1998/42)

Clapp's Cider Mill, Baltonsborough, 1930s.
(Courtesy of Mr R. Clapp; P1482)

Shovelling cider apples, Clapp's Cider Mill, 1930s. (Courtesy of Mr R. Clapp; P1484)

Coate's cider price list, 1928. (P2495)

Dorset Down ram lambs in an orchard, Manor Farm, Curry Rivel, c.1966.
(Courtesy of Mr A. Lang; 139/146)

Apple collecting machine, Baltonsborough, 1997.
(Courtesy of Mendip Hills AONB Service)

Strawberry pickers in the Cheddar area, 1900s. (P416, P417)

STRAWBERRIES

The Cheddar area, sheltered from the cold north and east winds by the Mendip Hills, is famous for growing strawberries. They were first commercially grown here at the end of the nineteenth century, traditionally on two or three acre market-garden smallholdings. From the early days the industry was organised to transport the strawberries to their markets in wooden chip baskets by rail. They are now packed in plastic punnets and travel by road.

1900s

The Royal Sovereign variety was introduced. This travelled well and allowed expansion of the industry.

1920s

As refrigerator boats replaced the live import of cattle and sheep at Avonmouth so supplies of cheap manure to fertilise the beds declined. In addition virus diseases on the increase throughout the country jeopardised the industry. The practice began of raising virus-free runners away from the main growing areas.

1960s

There were about 300 acres under strawberry cultivation, with specialised varieties used to produce an early crop under cloches, and a maincrop in the open.

1970s

An increase in the costs of seasonal labour required to pick the crop encouraged the use of cloches to extend the harvesting period and promoted the 'pick-your-own' system. Polythene tunnels were also being increasingly used instead of expensive glass cloches.

Loading chip baskets of strawberries onto a 'Strawberry Special' train, c.1900. (P415)

VILLAGES

Village life has altered enormously over the last hundred years. The coming of services such as electricity, telephone, and mains sewerage have made home life easier. Motor cars allow people to commute to work, and travel to do their shopping. Planning policy has determined where new houses can be built, and what they look like. Gradually the fabric of village life has altered. Two villages, both close to Glastonbury, each have their own different stories to tell.

Baltonsborough

BALTONSBOROUGH is a village and parish on the river Brue, 5 miles south-west from Glastonbury and 4 south-east from West Pennard station on the Somerset and Dorset joint railway, 3½ miles from Keinton Mandeville station on the Great Western railway, in the Wells parliamentary division, eastern division of Glaston Twelve Hides hundred, Glastonbury petty sessional division, Wells rural district and county court district, rural deanery of Glastonbury, archdeaconry of Wells and diocese of Bath and Wells. Baltonsborough is the birthplace of St. Dunstan, who, it is said, diverted the arm of the river Brue that flows by the churchyard to work the mill in Mill Street, the first corn mill in the neighbourhood and still working after 1,000 years. The church of St. Dunstan is a building of stone in the Late Pointed style, consisting of chancel, nave, south porch and an embattled western tower with pinnacles, containing a clock and 6 bells, all recast in 1804: the chancel retains its sedilia, which are ornamented with shields inclosed in panels, and there is an aumbry on the north side; the chancel walls have a richly-carved cornice, and there is a modern rood screen; the ceiling of the nave is waggon-shaped: the benches, dating from the 15th century, are of massive character; and the woodwork includes a stool of Jacobean date, said to have been formerly in use for offenders when doing penance: in the south wall of the nave is a piscina, and the church still keeps an hour-glass stand: the gables of the building exhibit some good mediæval crosses, and the tower roof displays fantastic metal work, wrought and affixed by a local smith: there are 200 sittings; a sanctuary knocker is on the church door; in the churchyard is a cross with a modern base and shaft, and an ancient crucifix head. The tower was restored in 1905 by subscription, at a cost of £650; at the same time the bells were re-hung by Mrs. Handley, of Bath, as a memorial to her husband, late curate of this parish, the church was restored in 1925 at a cost of £550. The register dates from the year 1538. The living is a vicarage, formerly annexed to that of Butleigh, but erected into a separate benefice in 1895, net yearly value £250, with residence, in the gift of Commdr. Ralph Neville R.N. (ret.), and held since 1929 by the Rev. Basil Grafton Richings M.A. of St. Edmund Hall, Oxford. There is a Methodist chapel, seating 100 persons. The Moravian chapel, erected in 1852, is a building of stone in the Gothic style, and will seat 250 persons; attached is a minister's house, built in 1859. On a plot of ground, purchased by the parishioners, at the cross roads, stands the memorial erected in 1922 to men of this parish who fell in the Great War, 1914-18. Orchard Neville is the property and residence of Maj. Bertrand Leland Thorp M.C., B.A. The trustees of the late William Benjamin Naish (d. 1885), who are lords of the manor, Edwin Austin esq. Mrs. Haine, Hungerford Clapp esq. and Robert Neville Grenville esq. D.L., J.P. are the chief landowners. Soil and subsoil, blue lias. The land is chiefly in pasture. The area is 2,709 acres of land and 11 of water; the population in 1931 was 474.

SOUTHWOOD is a small hamlet, 2 miles south-east. HAM STREET, a hamlet, a mile east. MILL STREET is a small hamlet, half a mile west.

Post, M. O., T. & T. E. D. Office. Letters through Glastonbury

Kelly's *Directory of Somerset*, 1935. (SCMS)

Baltonsborough, 1940s. (SCMS)

114

*'When electricity came we council tenants were offered three
free lights. I remember one downstairs and a Valor stove in
the kitchen. The room beyond had a bath and copper for washing.
Fire was lit beneath the copper and all household laundry
was boiled, with a blue bag to keep the colour, and starched.
It was lifted out with wooden tongs - no wringer.'*

Kathleen Vincent, speaking of the year 1936.

Back row far left: Bill Brougham, *far right:* Doug Bush
Middle row left to right: Mrs Brougham, Gladys Porter, pianist, and Vera Jenkins.
(Courtesy of Mr D. Bush)

The Follies

*'This party gave a most successful concert on Friday in the Schoolroom.
A great surprise awaited the audience when the curtains
were drawn, as the entire party were dressed in black and white
Pierrot costumes, the three ladies looking very chic in their dresses.'*

Central Somerset Gazette, 24 February, 1939.

V.J. Day celebrations outside the Greyhound Inn, 16 August, 1945. (Courtesy of Mrs P. Rendell)

Victory Celebrations

*'V.J. Day was celebrated in Baltonsborough by a decorated lorry,
representing H.M.S. Ballsbury touring the parish with band on board...
The day finished with a dance on Cross Roads, the roadway having
been floodlit by Messrs. B. Osborne and R. Flagg. Considering the
short notice a very enjoyable time was had by the large
crowd which had assembled.'*

Central Somerset Gazette, 24 August, 1945.

BALTONSBOROUGH

———

SUNDAY, NOVEMBER 6th, 1949,
at 10.50 a.m.

———

Order of Service

FOR THE

UNVEILING OF THE MEMORIAL

To the Men of this Parish who gave

their lives in the World War 1939—1945.

Order of Service, 1949. (SCMS)

'Mrs Jones stated that there is currently £95 in the
Welcome Home Fund and Comforts Fund. The aim is for £200.
Mr Joe Farrant proposed that a £5 gift should be given to
each local man serving in H.M. Forces and that a balance
should form a Memorial Fund to purchase a playing
field for the village.'

Parish Council Minutes, 28 April.

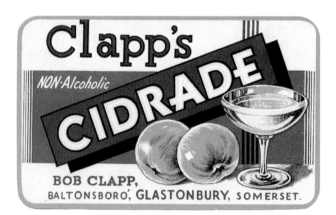

Cider bottle labels, 1940s. (SCMS)

Clapp's Cider Mill, Baltonsborough, 1930s. (Courtesy of Mr R. Clapp; P1485)

Local Cider Mill changes hands

*'Mr Clapp purchased the business in 1916, and during his
ownership the mills have been completely modernised throughout.
When he took over the fruit was pressed by hand; now all
this is done by electrically driven machinery.'*

Central Somerset Gazette, 6 September, 1946.

Farmers' float at Baltonsborough Horticultural Show, 1955. Joy Porter churning butter, Cecil Dunford making thatching spars. (Courtesy of Mr W. Dunkerton)

Farmers' float at Baltonsborough Horticultural Show, 1955. Maurice Dunkerton thatching, Dolly Dunkerton cheesemaking, Bill Dunkerton grafting apple trees. (Courtesy of Mr W. Dunkerton)

Successful innovation at Baltonsborough

'The Horticultural Society celebrated its golden jubilee a year ago, and on Saturday the 51st annual exhibition was held. A carnival was added to the day's attractions for the first time. It was a day of great and successful activity for the village, marred only by thunderstorms which developed at tea time which had an adverse effect on the evening's gymkhana programme.'

Central Somerset Gazette, 19 August, 1955.

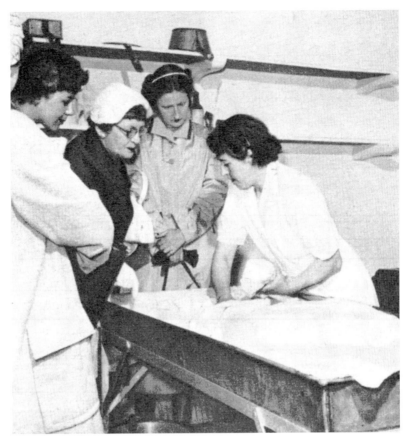

Miss Craig, in white hat, talks to Olive Tucker, head cheese-maker at Greenhill Farm, Baltonsborough, from an article in the *Farmer and Stock-Breeder*, 1955. (SCMS)

Baltonsborough Horticultural Show, 1956. *From left to right*: Bill Dunkerton, Clifford Vincent, Roy Lester, Ted Cotter. (Courtesy of Mrs Vincent)

Baltonsborough Horticultural Show prizewinner's certificate, 1956. (SCMS)

Shapwick

SHAPWICK is a village and parish, with a station, 2 miles north from the village on the Somerset and Dorset railway; it is 4½ miles west from Glastonbury, 8½ east from Bridgwater and 137½ from London, in the Bridgwater division of the county, hundred of Whitley, petty sessional division, rural district and county court district of Bridgwater, rural deanery of Glastonbury, archdeaconry of Wells and diocese of Bath and Wells. The church of St. Mary is a building of stone in the Early English and Perpendicular periods, consisting of chancel, nave, south porch and an embattled central tower containing 6 bells: in the chancel are mural tablets to the Bull and Strangways families, dating from 1657 up to recent years: the east and other windows of the chancel, the west window and those on the south side of the nave are stained: there are sittings for 250 persons. The register of baptisms and marriages dates from 1591; burials, 1590. The living is a vicarage, with that of Ashcott annexed, joint net yearly value £380, including 12 acres of glebe, and the interest from a further endowment in 1884 of £3,000 by Mrs. Strangways, sen. with residence, in the gift of Miss Vialls Strangways, and held since 1912 by the Rev. Charles Ernest Seamer M.A. of Brasenose College. Oxford. There are charities of £26 14s. 4d. annual value; this sum includes £13 13s. 8d. from Henry Smith's charity, and £8 6s. 8d. from Alexander's charity, which includes £4 3s. 4d. for education. Mineral springs, a holy well and hospital formerly existed on the site of the present Northbrook farm. The springs have been cut off, but the ancient building formerly containing the well still stands. Shapwick House, built upon the site of the old court house of Abbot John de Taunton by Judge Rolls about 1630, is now (1934) unoccupied, and Down House is the residence of Miss Vialls Strangways, who is lady of the rectorial manor and lay rector; value of rectorial tithes, £192. Mrs. Warry and Miss Vialls Strangways are the principal landowners. The soil is clayey and the subsoil stone. The chief crops are wheat, hay, beans and oats. The area is 3,562 acres of land and 5 of water; population in 1931, 275 in the civil parish and 951 in the ecclesiastical parish.

Post, M. O., T. & T. E. D. Office. Letters through Bridgwater. There is a T. office at the railway station for delivery on the station premises only, closed on sundays

Railway Station (Som. & Dor)

Kelly's *Directory of Somerset*, 1935. (SCMS)

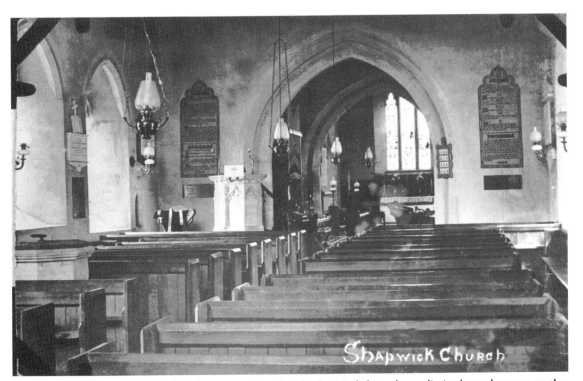

The hanging oil lamps in the church were replaced with electric lights when a limited supply came to the village in 1936. Some properties were not connected until the 1950s. (P3118)

Most cottages had open fires using local turf – now called peat.
In the 1930s turf cost one old penny a block. (P3275)

'In the 1930s few people had a car. The only way to go places and see a bit of the country was a trip in a charabanc.'
Dora Watkins. (P3104)

Shapwick House was used as a convalescent home for soldiers during the Second World War. The uniforms of blue suits and red ties were a familiar sight in the village. (P3109)

Shapwick Station, 6 April, 1959. The train for Highbridge. Brian Ellis is on the left.
(Courtesy of Joanes Publications; P3103)

'Keys on big loops were exchanged when each train arrived.'

Brian Ellis, signalman, describing how they ensured that the single track ahead was clear.

HILL FARMING

L and use on Exmoor and other western hills is characterised by sheep grazing on the open uplands. On Exmoor ponies were also a valuable commodity. Beef cattle are also important. In the nineteenth century the Knight family did much to enclose Exmoor 'Forest', establishing a series of model farms, but others were active elsewhere on the Moor in farming or enlarging small hill farms below the high moors, which to a large extent survive (if only just) today.

Weatherslade Farm at Withypool was a typical small Exmoor hill farm, unusual in that its owner – Fred Milton – lived to an enormous age and rarely parted with an implement once bought. The dispersal sale following his death revealed a treasure-trove of machinery.

Larkbarrow Farm, one of the Knight farmsteadings on the Forest of Exmoor.
(Exmoor Photographic Archive)

Dispersal sale at Weatherslade Farm, Withypool, 1999

(this page and opposite)

1950s manure spreader by Bamford
and supplied by Farmese. (P5131)

1950s Minor Mk 4 bailer by Jones Brothers of Mold.
(P5134)

1950s tractor by Ferguson. (P5132)

1950s Minor Mk 4 bailer by Jones Brothers of Mold. (P5134)

1940s reaper-binder by Albion. (P5135)

1940s Fordson Major tractor. (P5136)

1950s haysweep. (P5138)

Dispersal sale at Weatherslade Farm, Withypool, 1999

(this page and opposite)

1940s chaff cutter by Dening of Chard. (P5143)

1960s spring harrow. (P5144)

1960s elevator by Briggs & Stratton. (P5145)

1950s tedder by Nicholson. (P5146)

1940s two furrow tractor plough by Ransomes. (P5147)

1950s buck rake. (P5149)

George Fisher harrowing, Winsford, 1923. (Exmoor Photographic Archive)

The Exmoor Horn [the indigenous breed] Sheep Society at Winsford in 1908. (Exmoor Photographic Archive)

John Thomas and John Ridd of Yenworthy Farm, Oare, shearing in 1915.
(Exmoor Photographic Archive)

J. Bawden's Exmoors passing through Dulverton for Salisbury Plains

Exmoor Horn sheep being driven down to Dulverton Station for transhipment, passing through Dulverton around 1923. (Exmoor Photographic Archive)

The Young Farmers movement, which started in Devon in the 1920s and rapidly spread to Somerset, has been particularly important in remoter rural communities such as Exmoor. These Young Farmers are at a rally in Wootton Courtenay in 1936. (Exmoor Photographic Archive)

Exmoor ponies were traditionally gathered in the Autumn and sold at Bampton Fair in October, until the practice ceased in the 1980s. (Exmoor Photographic Archive)

The 'flying column' for Bampton gathers at the Crown Hotel, Exford, in 1920.
(Exmoor Photographic Archive)

Cross-bred Exmoor ponies being taken across Winsford Hill bound for Bampton, 1930.
(Exmoor Photographic Archive)

Priddy Sheep Fair, 1979. (P1195, P1196)

MARKET

The traditional destination for the farmers' livestock and crops was the local market, which was also an important social event. However, with the rise of food processing industries and supermarket outlets, farms have become increasingly detached from consumers. Distribution, packaging, advertising, and marketing industries have all grown up to add value to the product.

As livestock and crop intervention prices fall, traditional farmers are seeking to increase their profit margins by selling directly through farm shops and farmers' markets. They are also responding to the increasing demand for organic produce and high quality regional foods. The Somerset organic acreage quadrupled in the last four years of the twentieth century.

Tor Fair Market, Glastonbury, 1987. (S5766)

Sheep auction, Taunton Market, 1988. (Photographer Miss P. Peacock)

local produce for local people

Glastonbury Farmers' Market

St John's Car Park

9.30 a.m.-1.30 p.m.

Saturday

29 August ● 26 September ● 24 October

Sold by the producer

Quality   Freshness   Locally produced   Seasonal

Demos ● Live Entertainment ● Fun

Contact: Kate Hall, Local Agenda 21 Officer,
Mendip District Council Tel: 01749 343399

Leaflet advertising the first Glastonbury Farmers' Market, 1998. (SCMS)

First Glastonbury Farmers' Market, 1998. (SCMS)

ACKNOWLEDGEMENTS

I gratefully acknowledge help from the following:

Bertie Bond
Dickies (UK) Limited
Doug Bush
Bob Clapp
Allen Cotton
Bill Dunkerton
David Gwilliam
George Maidment
Jean Pope
Kathleen Vincent
Derrick Warren
Morris and Molly Winstone

Many individuals and farming families from across Somerset, and particularly from Baltonsborough and Shapwick, who have generously loaned their photographs.

Howard Joint and Ida Panter from the Edington Village Archive Group.

Louise Clapp, Dennis Hill-Cottingham, Ann Heeley, Sue Markham, Pat Meyer, Carol Soulsby, Elizabeth Smith, Doreen Venitt, Mary Vidal, Dora Watkins, and other Friends of the Somerset Rural Life Museum Research Group, especially for their contribution to the Villages section.

My colleagues in the Somerset County Museums Service, in particular Estelle Jakeman for researching work wear, Lawrence Bostock, David Dawson, John French and Mary Gryspeerdt.

Exmoor Photographic Archive
Mendip Hills AONB Service
Somerset Archives and Records Service
Somerset County Farms Estate
Somerset County Health and Safety Unit
Somerset County Sustainable Somerset Group
Somerset Local History Library

SOMERSET COUNTY MUSEUMS SERVICE

The Somerset County Museums Service has the role of providing a public service which collects, conserves, researches, communicates and exhibits material evidence of humankind and our natural environment with particular reference to the County of Somerset for the purposes of study, education and enjoyment.

It does this most noticeably through displays, exhibitions and activities at the Somerset County Museum in Taunton, Somerset Rural Life Museum in Glastonbury, and with other museums throughout Somerset and the South West. It also provides educational services for schools including a loans service, offers professional advice and other professional services, and promotes lifelong learning and training.

Collections of material evidence are at the core of the Service's activities, and the conservation, management and research of these collections are of prime importance. Although many of the collections are not on display the Service encourages access to them. Should you wish to consult the collections please contact the relevant curator.

Somerset County Museums Service

Telephone: 01823 320200

Website: www:somerset.gov.uk/museums